Duets for Fun

Guitars

Easy Pieces to Play Together

Edited by
Martin Hegel

ED 13883
ISMN 979-0-2201-3706-8
ISBN 978-1-84761-414-8

www.schott-music.com

Mainz · London · Berlin · Madrid · New York · Paris · Prague · Tokyo · Toronto
© 2016 SCHOTT MUSIC Ltd, London · Printed in Germany

Introduction

Anyone who opens this collection will discover some precious little gems in the form of original compositions for two guitars. The book offers a representative cross-section of easy to intermediate guitar duos from the Renaissance, Classical and Romantic to the present day. This selection is aimed at guitarists who have already acquired sound basic skills in playing the guitar: the pieces are suitable for playing in auditions, concerts and competitions. Each chapter contains some easy pieces and some at intermediate level. The majority of pieces are from the Classical period, known as the heyday of guitar music, where the choice is plentiful.

Repertoire intended as an adjunct to tuition has to focus in particular on certain aspects of duo playing, such as confidence in playing one's own part and developing awareness of the style and musical language of different periods. While taking care to produce an even tone, players need to listen closely to one another, improve technical and musical aspects of their own playing and learn to work on interpretation by playing together.

As ties and ornaments can represent a challenge, they are indicated as optional in this edition and recommended mainly to more advanced players, who may also choose to venture into higher positions or perhaps swap parts for repeats. In Renaissance pieces the use of scordatura has been omitted for the sake of easier reading.

I hope all you guitarists will enjoy making music together!

Martin Hegel
Translation Julia Rushworth

ED 13883
British Library Cataloguing-in-Publication Data.
A catalogue record for this book is available from the British Library
ISMN 979-0-2201-3706-8
ISBN 978-1-84761-414-8

English translation: Julia Rushworth
Cover design by www.adamhaystudio.com
Cover photography: iStockphoto.com
Printed in Germany · S&Co. 9307

Contents

Renaissance

Francis Pilkington (1565–1638)	1. Echo for two lutes	4
Francesco da Milano (1497–1543)	2. La Spagna	6
Anonymous (16th cent.)	3. Greensleeves	8
Anonym (16th cent.)	4. La Rossignol	10
Thomas Robinson (1560–1609)	5. A Toy for two lutes	11
Anonymous (16th cent.)	6. A Lesson for two lutes	13
Francesco da Milano	7. Canon for two lutes	14

Classical

Joseph Küffner (1776–1856)	8. Allemande	16
Ferdinando Carulli (1770–1841)	9. Ariette connue No. 7	18
Mauro Giuliani (1781–1829)	10. Ländler No. 11	20
Joseph Küffner	11. Duo No. 1	21
Ferdinando Carulli	12. Ariette connue No. 12	22
Fernando Sor (1778–1839)	13. Valse No. 1	24
Mauro Giuliani	14. Ländler No. 11	26
Joseph Küffner	15. Duo No. 3	27
Ferdinando Carulli	16. Le Nid et la Rose	28
Fernando Sor	17. Valse No. 2	30
Mauro Giuliani	18. La Pace	32
Leonhard von Call (1767–1815)	19. Rondo	34
Antoine de Lhoyer (1768–1852)	20. Nocturne No. 2	37

Romantic

Francisco Tárrega (1852–1909)	21. Vals para dos	40
Pierre Pettoletti (1800–1870)	22. Valse	42
Francisco Tárrega	23. Mazurka	43

Modern

Gerhard Maasz (1906–1984)	24. Duo No. 8	44
Olivier Mayran de Chamisso (b. 1955)	25. Lande celtique	46
Fritz Pilsl (b. 1933)	26. Tarantella	48
Friedrich Zehm (1923–2007)	27. Musette	50
Olivier Mayran de Chamisso (b.1955)	28. Promenade en barque	51
Gerhard Maasz (1906–1984)	29. Duo No. 6	54
Fritz Pilsl (b.1933)	30. Musette	56

Echo for two lutes

Francis Pilkington
(1565–1638)

1

La Spagna

Francesco da Milano
(1497–1543)

Greensleeves

Anonymous
(16th century)

from: The Dowland Lute Book (1610)

La Rossignol

Anonymous
(16th century)

from: The Pickering Lute Book (1616)

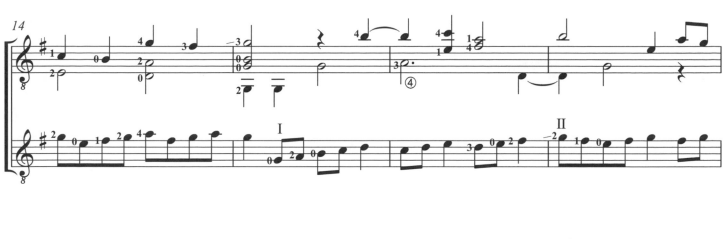

A Toy for two lutes

Thomas Robinson
(1560–1609)

from: The The Schoole of Musicke (1603)

A Lesson for two lutes

Anonymous
(16th century)

6

Canon for two lutes

Francesco da Milano
(1497–1543)

from: The Cavalcanti Lute Book

Allemande

Joseph Küffner
(1776–1856)

from: Joseph Küffner, 12 Duos Op. 87

TRIO

D. C. al Fine

Ariette connue No. 7

Ferdinando Carulli
(1770–1841)

from: Ferdinando Carulli, Choix de 24 Ariettes connus Op. 72

Ländler No. 11

Mauro Giuliani
(1781–1829)

from: Mauro Giuliani, 16 Ländler Op. 16a

Duo No. 1

Joseph Küffner

from: Joseph Küffner, 12 Duos Op. 87

Ariette connue No. 12

Ferdinando Carulli

from: Ferdinando Carulli, Choix de Ariettes connues Op. 72

Valse No. 1

Fernando Sor
(1778–1839)

13

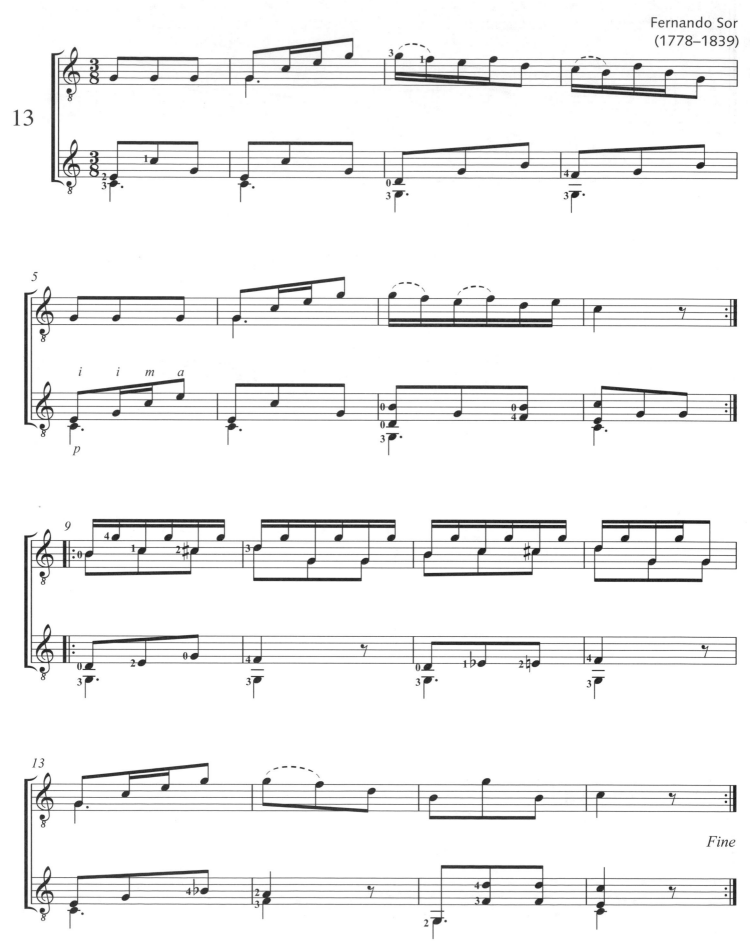

Fine

from: Fernando Sor, Six valses faciles Op. 44

D. C. al Fine

Ländler No. 11

Mauro Giuliani

14

from: Mauro Giuliani, 12 Ländler Op. 55

Duo No. 3

Joseph Küffner

from: Joseph Küffner, 12 Duos Op. 87

Le Nid et la Rose

Ferdinando Carulli

16

from: Ferdinando Carulli, 12 Romances Op. 333

Valse No. 2

Fernando Sor

from: Fernando Sor, Six valses faciles Op. 44bis

D. C. al Fine

La Pace

Mauro Giuliani

18

© 2016 SCHOTT MUSIC Ltd, London
from: Mauro Giuliani, Le aventure di amore Op. 116

Rondo

Leonhard von Call
(1767–1815)

from: Leonhard von Call, Duo facil Op. 20

Nocturne No. 2

Antoine de Lhoyer
(1768–1852)

Menuetto poco vivace

Fine

from: Antoine de Lhoyer, Six Duos nocturnes Op. 37

Vals para dos

Francisco Tárrega
(1852–1909)

Valse

Pierre Pettoletti
(1800–1870)

Grazioso

22

Mazurka

Francisco Tárrega
(1852–1909)

23

Fine

D. C. al Fine

Duo No. 8

Gerhard Maasz
(1906–1984)

24

from: Gerhard Maasz, 10 Easy Pieces
Schott GA 431

Lande Celtique

Olivier Mayran de Chamisso
(b. 1955)

from: Olivier Mayran de Chamisso, Rêveries en duo
Schott SF 1000

Tarantella

Fritz Pilsl
(b. 1933)

26

from: Fritz Pilsl, 7 Duos, Schott ED 7127

Musette

Friedrich Zehm
(1923–2007)

27

from: Friedrich Zehm, 11 Pieces for Beginners
Schott ED 6984

Promenade en barque

Olivier Mayran de Chamisso
(b. 1955)

from: Olivier Mayran de Chamisso, Rêveries en duo
Schott SF 1000

Duo No. 6

Gerhard Maasz
(1906–1984)

Musette

Fritz Pilsl

© 2016 SCHOTT MUSIC Ltd, London
from: F. Pilsl, 7 Duos, Schott GA 431

About the composers

Anonymous sources: The Sampson Lute Book (1610); The Jane Pickering Lute Book (1616); The Dowland Lute Book (1610); The Cavalcanti Lute Book (1590).

Leonhard von Call (1767-1815) was an Austrian composer and guitarist. While music was a hobby for him, he was nevertheless a popular composer whose works were published many times during his lifetime.

Ferdinando Carulli (1770–1841) was Neapolitan by birth. He settled in Paris and wrote about 350 works, including a widely used guitar tutor.

Mauro Giuliani (1781–1829) was one of the most notable guitar virtuosos of the 19th Century. He lived in Vienna from 1806, composed over 200 pieces and was the first composer to use polyphonic writing in guitar music.

Joseph Küffner (1776–1856) came from a family of musicians in Franconia, Northern Bavaria. After working as a violinist in the Würzburg court orchestra he became a bandmaster in a Bavarian regiment.

Antoine de Lhoyer (1768–1852) was a French composer and guitarist. For a long time he was employed as a musician at the court of the Tsar in St Petersburg. Most of his compositions were for chamber ensemble with guitar.

Gerhard Maasz (1906–1984) was a composer, pianist and conductor born in Hamburg. His music includes pieces for solo instruments, small ensembles and full orchestra.

Olivier Mayran de Chamisso (b.1955) was born in Versailles. A guitarist, composer and music teacher, he mainly writes for guitar and piano.

Francesco da Milano (1497–1543) was an Italian composer and lutenist. He was employed for a while in the service of Pope Leo X in Rome. His incomparable playing earned him the nickname *'il divino'* during his own lifetime.

Pierre Pettoletti (1800–1870) was probably born in Italy. Besides visiting Germany and Sweden, he spent most of his life in St Petersburg, working as a guitarist and teacher.

Francis Pilkington (1565–1638) was an English composer, lutenist and singer – notably as a chorister at Chester Cathedral.

Fritz Pilsl (b.1933) is a German composer who chiefly writes chamber music for the guitar with various combinations of instruments.

Thomas Robinson (1560–1609) was an influential English composer and teacher. For a time he was employed at the Danish court, where foreign musicians were often favoured. His book *'The Schoole of Musicke'* became the most important lute tutor published in England.

Fernando Sor (1778–1839) was born in Barcelona. He ranks as one of the finest and most notable guitar composers of the 19th Century. He acquired his musical training in a monastery and spent much of his life in Paris.

Francisco Tárrega (1852–1909) may be considered the most celebrated guitarist and composer of his day. He introduced important developments in guitar technique and his masterful compositions are among the most popular pieces in the guitar repertoire.

Friedrich Zehm (1923–2007) worked as a composer, pianist and music teacher. His music ranges from orchestral works and chamber music (particularly for wind instruments) to solo songs and choral pieces.

Baroque
Guitar Anthology

Original Works from the 17th and 18th centuries selected and transcribed for guitar by Jens Franke and Stuart Willis

Romantic
Guitar Anthology

Original Works and Transcriptions from the Romantic period selected and edited by Jens Franke

Volume 1	(Grades 1-2)	ED 13357
Volume 2	(Grades 3-4)	ED 13437
Volume 3	(Grades 5-6)	ED 13446
Volume 4	(Grades 7-8)	ED 13489

Volume 1	(Grades 1-2)	ED 13110
Volume 2	(Grades 3-4)	ED 13111
Volume 3	(Grades 5-6)	ED 13112
Volume 4	(Grades 7-8)	ED 13113

- Graded pieces, presented in a progressive order

- New transcriptions and pieces published for the first time

- Practice notes and commentary for each piece

- Composer biographies included

- CD recording of all the pieces played by Jens Franke

www.schott-music.com